Selections From
RUSSIAN
Poetry and Prose

Illustrated by Elizabeth Korolkoff

HARVEY HOUSE, INC.
Publishers
Irvington-on-Hudson, N. Y.

Selections From
RUSSIAN
Poetry and Prose

by VLADIMIR RUS

HARVEY HOUSE, INC.
Publishers
Irvington-on-Hudson, New York

Contents

Содержание

Foreword

The time has passed when knowledge of the Russian people was confined to reading Tolstoy, Dostoevsky and Chekhov. Today the statesman, the scientist, the businessman find it increasingly important to know what the Russians are doing, and how and why they are doing it.

In their respective fields, the leaders and the professional men may ask simple and practical questions. Yet the answers, in order to be practical, cannot be simple. They must be fashioned from the understanding of the heart and mind of a people who bestride the mountains separating Europe and the West from Asia. It is this twofold nature of their roots which makes their actions appear now familiar, now puzzling, but always with a flavor of their own.

This small volume offers samples of the rich heritage, so little known here, which distinguishes the Russian people. It is an invitation to become acquainted with the spirit and mystique of Russia, and so to begin to understand the desires and goals, the triumphs and failures of a great people.

DR. MARY EMERY
Hofstra University

May, 1965

Preface

This volume does not intend to fill a gap. It would like to help create one.

It is a random stroll through the fields of Russian letters which, for most Western readers, are still an unexplored territory. Like the mapmakers of old, we easily assume that whatever has not been explored either does not exist or else is inhabited by savages only. This little collection would like to suggest that the unknown territory of Russian literature contains much that is beautiful and much that is worth thinking about.

Some of the names are familiar even in the West. Most of them are not. That does not mean they have been dredged from the obscure ranks of Russian writers. They are all classics, or at least popular with every Russian who reads. And most Russians read.

There are many reasons why in comparison with other Western literatures Russian letters remain largely ignored. The most obvious ones are inaccessibility of the language and generally poor quality of translations.

Less obvious but more important is the difference between the spirit of the Russian writer and the spirit of his English speaking reader. England is an insular nation surrounded by the ocean, with its inhabitants confined to a small territory where by constant converse they have grown extrovert, urbane, superbly practical. Their language and literature reflect these qualities.

Other great Western literatures, though not insular, have yet been shaped by confinement to a geographically narrow and thus intellectually stimulating milieu of a city. Greek literature grew in Athens, Latin in Rome, Italian in Florence, French in Paris, German in Weimar. The city gave all of them the rational character which is a necessary condition of success in a tightly knit society.

By contrast, Russians have not lived on an island surrounded by the sea. They have lived on the endless sea itself, on the boundless Russian plain. It may be that their nation found for itself a place on earth which corresponded best to its innermost inclinations. Or again it may be that their land conveyed its character to their souls. However we explain it, the spirit of the plain is the spirit of Russia and the spirit of her literature. There is formlessness and irrationality, there is melancholy and languidity. There is the mystical urge of ever receding horizons. There are outbursts of energy sweeping like blizzards across the plains.

For a Western reader, then, it is not easy to like Russian literature. We acclaim as good literature that which expresses our humanity. We acclaim as great literature that which expresses it accurately and profoundly. But the expression must be always attuned to our thinking. And the Russian way of expression and the Russian mode of thinking are different from ours. Their literature, even though good, even though great, often fails to touch the Western reader because it has a modality to which we are not accustomed.

The selections offered here have been chosen with this difficulty in mind. They possess sufficient interest to be read for their own sake. At the same time they provide an insight into what is specifically Russian and can serve as a stimulus to further reading and better understanding of Russian works.

V. R.

If you love, go any length!
If you threaten, do not smile!
If you scold, with all your bile!
If you cut, with all your strength!

If you fight, make it a brawl!
If you punish, make it hot!
To forgive, with all your soul!
And to drink, swig like a sot!

Alexéy Konstantínovich Tolstóy (1817-75; a many-sided, serene idealist, the least tragic of all Russian poets).

Russians are often accused of being lazy. It is more accurate to say that they possess an energy which is not easily aroused, but once aroused, surges with elemental force. It is this energy which gives an air of tension and feverish expectation to their music and letters.

Коль любить...

Коль люби́ть, так без рассу́дку,
Коль грози́ть, так не на шу́тку,
Коль ругну́ть, так сгоряча́,
Коль рубну́ть, так уж сплеча́.

Коли́ спо́рить, так уж сме́ло,
Коль кара́ть, так уж за де́ло,
Коль прости́ть, так всей душо́й,
Коль пир, так уж пир горо́й.

Алексе́й К. Толсто́й

To My Children

In days long past, my children, when the shadows grew
Well into the night, I often came to you

To watch over your sleep in tender mood,
To think how innocent you are, how good.

And now I come again: In your room not a sound,
Your bed is empty, darkness all around.

So passed my life, so long my shadows grew—
Oh, children, pray for him who used to pray for you.

Alexéy Stepánovich Khomyakóv (1804-60; besides sonorous poetry he wrote works on history and on theology).

Russians have great reverence and affection for children. Only Walt Whitman dared to be as blunt and unselfconscious in his tenderness as are the Slavs.

Бывало...

Бывало, в глубокий полуночный час,
Малютки, приду любоваться на вас,

Стеречь умильно ваш детский покой,
Подумать о том, как вы чисты душой.

Теперь прихожу я: везде темнота,
Нет в комнате жизни, кроватка пуста.

О дети, в глубокий полуночный час
Молитесь о том, кто молился о вас.

Алексей С. Хомяков

Beyond the river, the swift river,
Smoke the ruins of towns.
The Tatar rascals take the towns,
Take the towns, divide the loot.
Each and every one gets something:
One gets gold, and one gets silver,
One a good horse, one a Russian maid.
A young swain obtained an aging mother,
And he took her by her white hands,
Put her in his carriage,
Carried her to his vast palace,
Shouted with loud voice,
Loud voice of a hero:
"Come to meet me, my young wife,
I have brought a Russian maid,
Russian maid, a prisoner.
Make her do three things:
First—embroider carpets,
Second—watch the geese,
Third—rock the children."
"With my hands I have embroidered,
With my eyes I watched the geese,
With my feet I rocked the child.
You hush-a-bye, my baby,
From your father you're a cruel Tatar,
Unchristened and unprayed for,
From your mother you're a little hero,
Russian hero, chip of Russian block."

Татарский плен

Злы татáрчёнки городá берýт,
Городá берýт, по себé дéлят,
Да комý что достáнется:
Комý зóлото, комý сéребро,
Комý дóбрый конь, комý нянюшка.
Доставáлася тёща зятюшке.
Зять берёт её за белы руки,
Посадил её во колясочку,
Подвозил её к ширóму дворý,
Вскрикнул грóмким гóлосом,
Грóмким гóлосом молóдецким:
— Ты встречáй меня, молодá женá,
Я привёз тебé рýсску нянюшку,
Рýсску нянюшку, нáшу плéнницу.
Ты застáвь её дéлать три делá:
Пéрвое дéло — коврý вышивáть,
Другóе дéло — гусéй стеречи́,
А трéтье — детéй качáть. —
— Я рукáми вышила,
Я глазáми гусéй стереглá,
Я ногáми дитю качáла:
Ты качý-баю, моё дитятко,
Ты по бáтюшке злóй татарчёнок,
Ты не крéщёнóй, не молитвеннóй,
А по мáмушке мой боярченок,
Мой боярченок, рýсска кóсточка. —

The young princess overheard this:
"How do you know, nurse-maid,
That he's a cruel Tatar from his father
But a Russian hero from his mother?"
"How should I fail to know, my daughter?
You were just seven when the Tatars caught you."

Anonymous

Old Russian songs ring often with reminders of the times when Russia was humiliated by Tatar invaders from Asia. For two hundred years Russians suffered under their yoke while Western Europe was fashioning its spiritual and mental tools in medieval universities and laying foundations of the modern society in its cities.

Услыха́ла молода́ княжна́:
— Почему́ зна́ешь, моя́ ня́нюшка,
Что по ба́тюшке — злой тата́рчёнок,
А по ма́тушке он боя́рченок? —
— Как мне не знать, моя до́ченька,
Ты семи́ лет во поло́н взята́. —

Аноним

Svyatogor

Svyatogor got ready for a ride in the fields,
He saddled his good horse,
He rode across the steppe.
He had no one with whom to measure his strength,
And his strength through his veins
Ran wild like a sprite.
His strength lay heavy on him like a crushing burden.
Lo! Svyatogor speaks:
"If I could find a place to stand,
I could lift up the whole earth."

Riding through the steppe, Svyatogor finds
A small saddle bag.
He takes his whip, pokes with it at the bag—it does not move.
He pushes it with his finger—it does not budge.
He grips it with his hand—it does not come up:
"Many years have I been riding through the world,
Such a wonder I have never found,
Such a miracle have never seen:
A small saddle bag, and yet
It does not move, it does not budge, it does not come up."

Svyatogor jumps off his good horse,
Grips the bag, lifts it up to his knees—

Святогор

Снаряди́лся Святого́р во чи́сто по́ле гуля́ти,
Заседла́ет своего́ добра́ коня́
И е́дет по чи́сту по́лю.
Не с кем Святого́ру си́лой померя́ться,
А си́ла то по жи́лочкам
Так жи́вчиком и перелива́ется.
Гру́зно от си́лушки как от тяжёлого бре́мени.
Вот и говори́т Святого́р:
— Как бы я тя́ги нашёл,
Так я бы всю зе́млю подня́л! —

Наезжа́ет Святого́р в степи́
На ма́ленькую су́мочку перемётную.
Берёт погоня́лку, пощу́пает су́мочку — она́ не сдвига́ется.
Дви́нет персто́м её — не ше́вельнётся.
Хва́тит с коня́ руко́ю — не поды́мется:
— Мно́го годов я по све́ту е́зживал,
А э́такого чу́да не нае́зживал,
Тако́ва чу́да не ви́дывал.
Ма́ленькая су́мочка перемётная,
Не сдвига́ется, не шевельнётся. —

Слеза́ет Святого́р с добра́ коня́,
Ухвати́л он су́мочку повы́ше коле́н:

Up to his knees into the earth he sank,
Down his white face not tears, but blood is rolling.
Where he sank, there he could not get up,
There he found his death.

Anonymous (from the Russian heroic songs, 9th and 10th cent.)

One of the most popular themes of world literature symbolizing the ironies of life is the death of a hero caused by some trivial incident. Achilles dies because he is shot in the heel, Siegfried because a leaf had fallen on his back, Samson because his hair had been cut; David defeats Goliath with a pebble, the Nordic god of thunder succumbs in a wrestling match to an old woman. In the death of Svyatogor, this ironic theme is heightened to absurdity: he could lift the whole earth but dies trying to budge an empty saddle bag.

И по колéна Святогóр в зéмлю угря́з,
А по бéлу лицý не слёзы, а кровь течёт.
Где Святогóр угря́з, тут и встать не мог,
Тут емý бы́ло и кончáние.

Аноним

River most sacred of all,
Empress mother of crystal-clear waters,
Am I bold enough, on my weak harp
To sing of you, Volga?

As fierce and terrible as you are
In your majesty, O Volga,
So dear and beautiful are you in your goodness.
You are God's image in this world!
Flow! Make Russia beautiful!
Whisper, you holy river,
Make your greatness known
Until the hand of time
Drains out your bed. . .
Alas! Not even you can escape
That bitter fate,
Even for you the end of time must come.
But long before then, many nations
Shall have withered, turned to dust,
And the radiance of living nature
Shall have died out on your banks.

Nikoláy Mikháylovich Karamzín (1766-1826; a sensitive poet of Rousseau's school, the first one in Russia to turn in poetry to his inner life).

The devotion of the Russian to the Volga, his holy river, is tender and fierce. Karamazín's poem represents well a sentiment which the whole nation shares.

Волга

Река́ свяще́ннейшая в ми́ре,
Криста́льных вод цари́ца-ма́ть!
Дерзну́ ли я, на сла́бой ли́ре
Тебя́, о Во́лга, велича́ть?

Сколь ты в вели́чии своём,
О Во́лга, я́ростна, ужа́сна,
Столь в бла́гости мила́, прекра́сна:
Ты о́браз Бо́жий в ми́ре сём.
Теки́, Росси́ю украша́я.
Шуми́, свяще́нная река́,
Свою́ вели́кость прославля́я,
Доко́ле вре́мени рука́
Не истощи́т твое́й пучи́ны . . .
Увы́! Сей го́рестной судьби́ны
И ты не мо́жешь избежа́ть:
И ты должна́ свой век сконча́ть!
Но пре́жде мно́гие наро́ды
Истле́ют, превратя́тся в прах,
И блеск цвету́щия приро́ды
Поме́ркнет на твои́х брега́х.

Никола́й М. Карамзи́н

Have you seen, ancient singer,
How in early spring in meadows
Russian girls dance their reel
To the tune of shepherd's flute?
How with bowed heads walk in circle,
With their boots they stamp in rhythm?
How they move their hands, their eyes,
With their shoulders how they speak?
How beneath their golden ribbons
Shine their brows, as white as snow? ...
Black like sable are their eyebrows,
Full of sparks the falcon eyes,
Smiling conquer easily
Lion's souls and hearts of eagles.
If you saw those pretty maidens,
You'd forget your Attic women,
And your Eros, with his wings
Of sweet passion, would be captured.

Gavríl Románovich Derzhávin (1743-1816; a dashing soldier of Tatar origin, a favorite court poet who wrote forceful and colorful lyrics).

Since 1587, the Russian peasant was held in bondage by the nobleman and the country squire. But on the banks of his holy river, life had its charmed moments. This sensuous poem captures admirably the characteristic movements of the Russian folk dancers.

Русские девушки

Зрел ли ты, певец ты дре́вний,
Как в лугу́ весно́й бычка́
Пля́шут де́вушки росси́йски
Под свире́лью пастушка́?
Как, склоня́сь глава́ми, хо́дят,
Башмака́ми в лад стуча́т,
Ти́хо ру́ки, взор пово́дят,
и плеча́ми говоря́т?
Как их ле́нтами златы́ми
Че́лы бе́лые блестя́т?
Как их бро́ви соболи́ны,
По́лный искр соко́лий взгляд,
их усме́шка ду́ши льви́ны
И орло́в сердца́ разя́т?
Коль бы ви́дел дев сих кра́сных,
Ты б греча́нок позабы́л
И на кры́льях сладостра́стных
Твой Эро́т прико́ван был.

Гаврии́л Р. Держа́вин

A Song

Little bird flies,
Little bird plays,
Little bird sings.
Little bird flew,
Little bird played,
He is no more.
Where are you, little bird?
Where, you little minstrel?
In a faraway land
You build now your nest,
There you sing now
Your merry song.

Vasíly Andréyevich Zhukóvsky (1783-1857; writer of light and melodious lyrics, great translator of Western European poets).

The musical gifts of the Russian people found their conscious expression in thousands of literary songs which range from charming trifles to songs heavy with thought.

Птичка

Птичка летает,
Птичка играет,
Птичка поёт;
Птичка летала,
Птичка играла,
Птички уж нет!
Где же ты, птичка,
Где ты, певичка?
В дальнем краю
Гнёздышко вьёшь ты,
Там и поёшь ты,
Песню свою.

Василий А. Жуковский

Winter

Hello there, in your white dress
Of silver brocade.
Diamonds are aflame all over you
Like brilliant sunrays.
Hello there, my Russian girl,
My beautiful maiden,
My snow-white swan,
Hello there, Mother Winter!
We don't fear your raw snows,
And with them our old friend frost,
Our blood brother, clever builder
Of bridges across our rivers
And of roads for sleighs and sledges.
You're our beauty and our fame,
You're our pleasant entertainment,
Brisk Russian winter!

Pëter Andréyevich Vyázemsky (1792-1878; a brilliant champion of Russian romanticism).

Perhaps it was the long, harsh winter that taught Russians their patience and gave them their ability to look for joy in the teeth of danger and death. Perhaps the harshness of the climate is one of the reasons why their joy is never free from melancholy strains.

Зима

Здра́вствуй, в бе́лом сарафа́не
Из сере́бряной парчи́!
На тебе́ горя́т алма́зы,
Сло́вно я́ркие лучи́.
Здра́вствуй, ру́сская моло́дка,
Раскраса́вица-душа́,
Белосне́жная лебёдка,
Здра́вствуй, ма́тушка-зима́!
Нам не стра́шен снег суро́вый,
С сне́гом ба́тюшка моро́з —
Наш приро́дный, наш дешёвый
Парохо́д и парово́з.
Ты у нас краса́ и сла́ва,
На́ша си́ла и казна́,
На́ша бо́драя заба́ва,
Молоде́цкая зима́!

Пётр А. Вя́земский

Do you want to be a judge? Just put on a fancy wig,
Scoff at those who plead a case and forget to grease your palm,
Teach your heart to flout the tears of the poor. Then take a nap
While your scribe drones out summations in an endless boring psalm.
And if someone mentions to you Civil Rights or Common Law,
Spit in his face! Say he's raving, trying to weigh down the judge
With such burdens. All you do is to sleep and pass the sentence
While onto the paper mountain climbs the scribe, your faithful drudge.

Antioch Kantemír (1708-44; a representative of the cosmopolitan enlightenment, he was published in French translations long before his first edition in Russian).

The strident note of satire and irony has never been absent from Russian letters. This 18th century imitation of Horace is close to the spirit of Roman and English satirists: it flagellates the office holder, not the office.

Хо́чешь ты судёю стать? Вздень пари́к с узла́ми,
Брани́ того́, кто проси́т с пусты́ми рука́ми,
Твёрдо се́рдце бе́дных пусть слёзы презира́ет,
Спи на сту́ле, когда́ дьяк вы́писки чита́ет.
Если ж кто вспо́мнит тебе́ гражда́нски уста́вы,
Иль есте́ственный зако́н иль наро́дны нра́вы,
Плюнь ему в ро́жу! Скажи́, что врёт околёсну,
Налага́я на суде́й ту тя́гость несно́сну,
Что подья́чим до́лжно лезть на бума́жны го́ры,
А судье́ дово́льно знать крепи́ть пригово́ры.

Антио́х Кантеми́р

The Swine and the Oak

Under an old Oak a Swine
Filled herself with acorns so that she could hardly walk;
After her feast she slept in the shade.
Blinking with her eyes, she woke up
And began to root under the Oak.
"Look, you're hurting him,"
A Crow told her from a branch.
"If you dig out his roots, he will die."
"Why, so let him die," she grunted blithely,
"That's of no concern to me,
Why he should exist, I know not.
If he did not stand here, what would change?
All I need are acorns. That's what makes me fat."
"Ingrate," spoke to her the Oak,
"If your snout allowed you to look up,
Perhaps you would notice
That those acorns grow on me."

Even so an ignorant
Blindly scoffs at study, learning,
At all works of human mind,
Knowing not, that of their fruits he eats.

Iván Andréyevich Krylóv (1769-1844; a librarian in St. Petersburg who made himself the voice of the middle-class outlook on life).

The tone is familiar: it is Aesop and La Fontaine in Russian feathers. But Krylóv was not satisfied with poking fun at human foibles. He struck out in sharp satire against the privileged nobleman.

Свинья под дубом

Свинья́ под ду́бом вековы́м
Нае́лась жо́лудей досы́та, до отва́ла.
Нае́вшись, вы́спалась под ним.
Пото́м, глаза́ продра́вши, вста́ла
И ры́лом подрыва́ть у ду́ба ко́рни ста́ла.
«Ведь э́то де́реву вреди́т»,
Ей с ду́ба во́рон говори́т,
«Коль ко́рни обнажи́шь, оно́ засо́хнуть мо́жет».
«Пусть со́хнет», говори́т Свинья́,
«Ничу́ть меня́ то не трево́жит,
В нём про́ку ма́ло ви́жу я.
Хоть век его́ не будь, ни чуть не пожале́ю,
Лишь бы́ли б жо́луди: ведь я от них жире́ю».
«Неблагода́рная!», промо́лвил дуб ей тут:
«Когда́ бы вверх могла́ подня́ть ты ры́ло,
Тебе́ бы ви́дно бы́ло,
Что э́ти жо́луди на мне расту́т».

Неве́жда так же в ослепле́ньє
Брани́т нау́ки и уче́нье
И все учёные труды́,
Не чу́вствуя, что он вкуша́ет их плоды́.

Ива́н А. Крыло́в

Russian Hospitality

(Selection from "Demian's Soup")

"Welcome, friend!
Have some soup!"—
                    "I am full."—
                                "Don't you stand

On ceremonies. Fall to! Eat!
Full of meat
Is this soup, the richest bowl
You have seen."—
                    "I ate just now."—
                                "Eat up all!

As long as there's a will. . .
It's so fat! Stuff your gizzard to the gill!
Come here, mother! Bring the dish
With cold salmon. Here! Some fish!"

Alex entertains his neighbor Percy
Without mercy.
Percy swims in sweat,
But not to hurt his pal he eats the fat,
Cleans the dish,
Eats the fish,
And when finished, is half dead.
Alex shouts: "That's my boy!
That's the way! It's a joy
Just to watch you. Let me pour another!
Where are the dumplings, mother?"

Русское гостеприимство

«Сосе́душка, мой свет!
Пожа́луйста, поку́шай». —
«Сосе́душка, я сыт по го́рло». —

　　　　「Ну́жды нет,

Ещё таре́лочку, послу́шай:
Уши́ца, ей-же-ей, на сла́ву сварена́!»
«Я три таре́лки съел». —

　　　　«И, по́лно, что за счёты:

Лишь ста́ло бы охо́ты, —
А то во здра́вье: ешь до дна!
Что за уха́! Да как жирна́:
Как бу́дто янтарём подёрнулась она́.

Поте́шь же, ми́ленький дружо́чек!
Вот сте́рляди кусо́чек!
Ещё хоть ло́жечку! Да кла́няйся, жена́!»
Так по́тчевал сосе́д-Демья́н сосе́да-Фо́ку
И не дава́л ему́ ни о́тдыху, ни сро́ку;
А с Фо́ки уж давно́ кати́лся гра́дом пот.
Одна́ко же ещё таре́лку он берёт:
Сбира́ется с после́дней си́лой
И — очища́ет всю. «Вот дру́га я люблю́!»
Вскрича́л Демья́н: «Зато́ уж чва́нных не терплю́.
Ну, ску́шай же ещё таре́лочку, мой ми́лой!»

Percy loves to eat
But he knows: this is the time to beat retreat.
And he waddles, while the waddling's good
From under the avalanche of food
Heading home, determined in his pain:
"Ne'er again."

Iván Andréyevich Krylóv

Тут бе́дный Фо́ка мой,
Как ни люби́л уху́, но от беды́ тако́й,
Схватя́ в оха́пку
Куша́к и ша́пку,
Скоре́й без па́мяти домо́й —
И с той поры́ к Демья́ну ни ного́й.

Ива́н А. Крыло́в

Prayer

Don't accuse me, Almighty,
Do not punish me, I pray,
That I love the lurid gloom of earth
And all her sorrows,
That the stream of Living Word
Rarely enters my soul,
That my erring reason wanders
On paths far removed from You,
That my breast heaves like volcanoes
With the lava of desires,
And that savage sentiments
Overcast my crystal eyes,
That this world I find too narrow,
But, afraid of penetrating to You,
I pray oft in sinful verses,
Oh, my God, but not to You.

Michael Yúrievich Lérmontov (1814-41; a soldier-poet, he ranged from Byronic romanticism to Russian folklore).

Though not an equal of his brilliant contemporary Púshkin, Lérmontov wrote profoundly moving poetry appealing to the innermost chords of the Russian heart. Here he presents himself as a man of ironic contradictions, suspended between faith and unbelief, aware of God and yet torn from him by his towering passions.

Молитва

Не обвиняй меня, Всесильный,
И не карай меня, молю,
За то, что мрак земли могильный
С её страстями я люблю ,
За то, что редко в душу входит
Живых речей твоих струя,
За то, что в заблужденьи бродит
Мой ум далёко от тебя,
За то, что лава вдохновенья
Клокочет на груди моей,
За то, что дикис волненья
Мрачат стекло моих очей,
За то, что мир земной мне тесен,
К тебе ж проникнуть я боюсь,
И часто звуком грешных песен
Я, Боже, не тебе молюсь.

Михаил Ю. Лермонтов

Russia

You cannot understand Russia with logic,
You cannot measure her with common yardstick.
She has a nature of her own,
You can only believe in her.

Fëdor Ivánovich Tyútchev (1803-73; the first Russian symbolist).

"The Russian soul has been fashioned out of our endless, formless plain," said Fëdor Stepun, a brilliant analyst of the Russian character.

Умо́м Росси́ю не поня́ть,
Арши́ном о́бщим не изме́рить:
У ней осо́бенная стать —
В Росси́ю мо́жно то́лько ве́рить.

Фёдор И. Тютчев

To My Nurse

Friend of my youth,
My tattered dove,
From days uncouth
My dearest love!
Alone you dwell
In forests deep,
And in your cell
Long watch you keep;
Your needles go
In wrinkled hands
Now fast, now slow. . .
You look askance
Out to the gate,
The untrod road,
And wait, and wait. . .
Long years have sowed
Worry and fear
Into your breast:
Unless I'm near
You cannot rest.

Alexander Sergéyevich Púshkin (1799-1837)

Púshkin, known in the West principally as the author of
Eugene Onegin, *was one of Russia's greatest poets.*

*His poems wittily and elegantly mirror Russian character
and attitudes. His lifelong devotion to his nurse and friend,
Arina Rodionovna, is expressed in many poems.*

Няне

Подру́га дней мои́х суро́вых,
Голу́бка дря́хлая моя́,
Одна́ в глуши́ лесо́в сосно́вых
Давно́, давно́ ты ждёшь меня́.
Ты под окно́м свое́й светли́цы
Горю́ешь бу́дто на часа́х,
И ме́длят помину́тно спи́цы
В твои́х намо́рщенных рука́х.
Гляди́шь в забы́тые воро́ты
На чёрный отдалённый путь:
Тоска́, предчу́вствия, забо́ты
Тесня́т твою́ всечасно грудь.

Алекса́ндр С. Пу́шкин

Epigram

"All is mine," said the gold,
"All is mine," said the sword;
"All I buy," said the gold,
"All I take," said the sword.

Alexander Sergéyevich Púshkin

Золото и булат

«Всё моё», — сказа́ло зла́то.
«Всё моё», — сказа́л була́т.
«Всё куплю́», — сказа́ло зла́то.
«Всё возьму́», — сказа́л була́т.

Алекса́ндр С. Пу́шкин

Citizen

I am a citizen! In our portentous days
Am I to blot this dignity of mine
By imitating your effeminate ways,
You fanciers of women and of wine?

Sweet are the arms of love. But only shame
They bring to those who strum the lovelorn lute
And let their fiery souls pine without flame,
And let a despot crush them underfoot.

They shall repent, when people raise their fight
And find them slaves to Venus, flaccid, soft,
Find none to champion the sacred right,
To hold the flag of liberty aloft.

Kondráty Fëdorovich Ryléyev (1795-1826)

*Less than six months after writing this poem, Ryléyev
was executed for participation in the December revolution, the
first violent attempt to solve the inner contradictions of Russia.*

Гражданин

Я ль бу́ду в роково́е вре́мя
Позо́рить Граждани́на сан
И подража́ть тебе́, изне́женное пле́мя
Перероди́вшихся славя́н?

Нет, не спосо́бен я в объя́тьях сладостра́стья,
В посты́дной пра́здности влачи́ть свой век младо́й
И изныва́ть кипя́щею душо́й
Под тя́жким и́гом самовла́стья.

Они́ раска́ются, когда́ наро́д, восста́в,
Заста́нет их в объя́тьях пра́здной не́ги
И, в бу́рном мятеже́ ища́ свобо́дных прав
В них не найдёт ни Бру́та, ни Рие́ги.

Кондра́тий Ф. Рыле́ев

Homeland

Even our land is an abomination.
The earth itself thinks in our nation
That to be high means to be insolent:
Our fields are humble, flat, obedient.
The huts cave in, the pubs are doing well!
Roads, which, if anywhere, lead to hell!
Our peasants tricked out in their rags
Squiring potbellied, barefooted hags.
Church steeples round, imitating syringes
So faithfully, my sense of beauty cringes.
What a view from the manor! It would seem
The squire is indulging in a stupid whim:
Dirt sticks, stench stinks, cockroaches crawl. Brains sleep—
And all this rules the master with his whip.
And this is what some morons call
Our "Mother Russia, Holiest Of All."

Dmítry Vladímirovich Venevítinov (1805-27; before his untimely death one of the brightest promises of Russian letters).

Serfdom was a disease rotting the roots of the country: Russians were held in bondage by Russians, and the whole nation suffered. The intellectuals were frustrated.

Родина

Приро́да на́ша, то́чно, ме́рзость!
Смире́нно пло́ские поля́ —
В Росси́и са́мая земля́
Счита́ет высоту́ за де́рзость —
Дрянны́е и́збы, кабаки́,
Брюха́тых баб босы́е но́ги,
В ла́птях дыря́вых мужики́,
Непроходи́мые доро́ги,
Да шпи́цы ве́чные церкве́й, —
С клисти́рных тру́бок сни́мок ве́рный,
С домо́в госпо́дских вид мизе́рный,
Грязь, ме́рзость вонь и тарака́ны,
И на́до всем хозя́йский кнут —
И вот что мно́гие болва́ны
«Свяще́нной ро́диной» зову́т.

Дми́трий В. Веневи́тинов

Prophecy

The year will come, that black Russian year
When into dust shall fall the imperial crown,
And rabble shall forget its past love for the Czars,
And many men shall feed on death and blood;
When, overthrown, the law shall cease to shield
Children, innocent women;
When Pestilence, arising from decaying corpses
Shall roam among the saddened villages
To summon life to death with a wave of his scarf
And Hunger shall begin to torture the poor land;
When waves of rivers shall grow red with flames.
On that day shall appear a mighty man,
You'll know him, and shall understand
Why he a sword of steel holds in his hand.
And woe to you! Your cries and moans
Shall seem to him ridiculous—
In him all shall be horrible and dark.

Michael Yúrievich Lérmontov (1814-41)

Only a Russian could have gauged as accurately the violence in the blood of the Russian serf as Lérmontov did in this poem written almost a hundred years before the revolution of 1917.

Предсказание

Настанет год, России чёрный год,
Когда царей корона упадёт.
Забудет чернь к ним прежнюю любовь,
И пища многих будет смерть и кровь,
Когда детей, когда невинных жён
Низвергнутый не защитит закон,
Когда чума от смрадных, мёртвых тел
Начнёт бродить среди печальных сел,
Чтобы платком из жизни вызывать,
И станет глад сей бедный край терзать,
И зарево окрасит волны рек:
В тот день явится мощный человек.
И ты его узнаешь и поймёшь,
Зачем в его руке булатный нож:
И горе для тебя! — твой плач, твой стон
Ему тогда покажется смешон.
И будет всё ужасно, мрачно в нём.

Михаил Ю. Лéрмонтов

She was harvesting on her master's field—
Now quietly she walked back to the sheaves.
Not to rest, though she was tired—
Just to feed her child.
He lay in the shade and cried.
She unwrapped his swaddling,
Fed him, rocked him, loved him—
And by and by she sang herself to sleep,
And dreamed: satisfied with his life
Is her Ivan... Handsome, rich,
And married, so it seemed, to a free woman,
And then, that even he himself was free...
With joyful faces do they harvest now
Wheat in their own field
And children bring them lunch...
And softly smiled the harvestwomen.
And then she woke... How heavy was her heart!
She wrapped her baby's swaddling hastily
And took her sickle, quickly to finish
Her quota of sheaves for the overseer.

Tarás Grigórevich Shevchénko (1814-61)

The Ukrainian (or Little Russian) Shevchénko would have probably lived and died as an unknown serf if Russian poet Zhukóvsky had not recognized his talent, bought him for 2,500 roubles and given him education. But even as a "free" man he was persecuted for his inflammatory verses and died after a ten years' forced service in the army.

Жница

Она́ на по́ле ба́рском жа́ла —
И ти́хо побрела́ к снопа́м.
Не отдохну́ть, хоть и уста́ла,
А покорми́ть ребёнка там.
В тени́ лежа́л и пла́кал он.
Она́ его́ распелена́ла —
Корми́ла, ня́нчила, ласка́ла —
И незаме́тно впа́ла в сон
И сни́тся ей, житьём дово́льный
Её Ива́н . . . Приго́ж, бога́т,
На во́льной, ка́жется, жена́т —
И потому́, что сам уж во́льный . . .
Они́ с лицо́м весёлым жнут
На поле́ со́бственном пшени́цу,
А де́тки им обе́д несу́т . . .
И ти́хо улыбну́лась жни́ца.
Но тут просну́лась . . . Тя́жко ей!
И, спелена́в малю́тку бы́стро,
Взяла́сь за серп, — дожа́ть скоре́й
Уро́чный сноп свой до бурми́стра.

Тара́с Г. Шевче́нко

I walked down the street. A beggar stopped me, an old man in rags. Bleary, teary eyes, livid lips, shaggy rags, suppurating scars. . . How horribly had poverty gnawed on this pitiful being!

He stretched out to me his red, swollen, dirty hand. He was moaning, groaning for help.

I searched my pockets. . . No wallet, no watch, not even a handkerchief. I had not taken anything with me.

And the beggar was waiting, his extended hand quivered and swayed. Bewildered, confused, I shook vigorously this dirty trembling hand. "Forgive me, brother; I have nothing with me." The beggar looked at me with his bleary eyes; his livid lips parted in a faint smile, and in his turn he pressed my cold fingers.

"No matter, brother," he lisped, "this also is a gift."

And I understood that I, too, had received a gift from my brother.

Iván Sergéyevich Turgénev (1818-83; famous in the West principally for his thoughtful novel Fathers and Sons).

Я проходи́л на у́лице ... меня́ останови́л ни́щий, дря́х-лый стари́к.

Воспалённые, слезли́вые глаза́, посине́лые гу́бы, шер-ша́вые лохмо́тья, нечи́стые ра́ны ... О, как безобра́зно обглода́ла бе́дность э́то несча́стное существо́!

Он протя́гивал мне кра́сную, опу́хшую, гря́зную ру́-ку ... Он стона́л, он мыча́л о по́мощи.

Я стал ша́рить у себя́ во всех карма́нах ... Ни ко-шелька́, ни часо́в, ни да́же платка́ ... Я ничего́ не взял с собо́ю.

А ни́щий ждал ... и протя́нутая рука́ его́ сла́бо колы-ха́лась и вздра́гивала.

Поте́рянный, смущённый, я кре́пко пожа́л э́ту гря́з-ную, тре́петную ру́ку ... «Не взыщи́, брат, нет у меня́ ни-чего́».

Ни́щий уста́вил на меня́ свои́ воспалённые глаза́. Его́ си́ние гу́бы усмехну́лись, и он в свою́ о́чередь сти́снул мои́ похолоде́вшие па́льцы.

— Что же, брат, — прошамкал он, — и на том спа-си́бо. Это то́же подая́ние, брат.

Я по́нял, что и я получи́л подая́ние от моего́ бра́та.

Ива́н С. Турге́нев

The Dog

We are two in the room: my dog and I. A violent storm rages outside.

The dog sits in front of me and looks straight into my eyes.

And I look into his.

It seems that he wants to tell me something. He is mute, he has no words, he does not understand himself—but I understand him.

I understand that in this moment there lives in both of us one and the same feeling, that there is no difference between him and me. We are identical. In each one of us burns and glows the same unsteady flame.

Death comes and brushes against that flame with her cold, sweeping wing. . .

And all is finished.

Who will then tell which flame was burning in me, and which in him?

No, it is not a beast and a man who contemplate each other. It's two pairs of identical eyes gazing at themselves.

And in each of these two pairs, in the beast and in the man, one and the same life clings timidly to the other.

Iván Sergéyevich Turgénev

Собака

Нас двóе в кóмнате: собáка моя́ и я. На дворé вóет стрáшная, неи́стовая бýря.

Собáка сиди́т пéредо мнóю — и смóтрит мне пря́мо в глазá.

Я тóже гляжý ей в глазá.

Она́ слóвно хóчет сказáть мне чтó-то. Онá немáя, онá без слов, онá самá себя́ не понимáет — но я её понимáю.

Я понимáю, что в э́то мгновéние и в ней и во мне живёт однó и то же чýвство, что мéжду нáми нет никакóй рáзницы. Мы тóжественны, в кáждом из нас гори́т и свéтится тот же трéпетный огонёк.

Смерть налети́т, махнёт на негó свои́м холóдным ширóким крылóм...

И конéц!

Кто потóм разберёт, какóй и́менно в кáждом из нас горéл огонёк?

Нет — э́то не живóтное и не человéк меня́ются взгля́дами.

Это две пáры одинáковых глаз устремлённы друг на дрýга.

И в кáждой из э́тих пар, в живóтном и человéке, однá и та же жизнь жмётся пугли́во к другóй.

Ивáн С. Тургéнев

When I die, bury me
In my Ukraine;
In the wide prairie
Dig out my grave
So that I may lie on a hill
Above the mighty river,
So that I may hear how old Dniepr rolls
His waves below the steep bank.

And when from the fields of the Ukraine
Old Dniepr shall carry the blood of our enemies,
Then even I will arise
From my grave,
I will arise and ascend
To God's threshold
To say a prayer there. Until that day
I know no God.

Bury me. But yourselves arise,
Break your chains,
Water your freedom
With the warm blood of your foes.

Завещание

Как умру́ — похорони́те
На Украи́не ми́лой,
Посреди́ широ́кой сте́пи
Вы́ройте моги́лу.
Чтоб лежа́ть мне на курга́не
Над реко́й могу́чей,
Чтобы слы́шать, как бушу́ет
Ста́рый Днепр под кру́чей!

И когда́ с поле́й Украи́ны
Кровь враго́в посты́лых
Понесёт он — вот тогда́ я
Вста́ну из моги́лы.
Поднилу́сь я и дости́гну
Бо́жьего поро́га —
Помоли́ться.. А поку́да
Я не зна́ю Бо́га!

Схорони́те и встава́йте,
Це́пи разорви́те,
И горя́чей вра́жьей кро́вью
Во́лю окропи́те.

And in the great family,
In the new, free family
Don't forget me, remember me
With a gentle, kind word.

Tarás Grigórevich Shevchénko (1814-61)

Shevchénko returned from his military service a broken man who had only four years to live. His admirers fulfilled his wish expressed in the "Testament" and buried him on a hill overlooking the Dniepr river.

61

И меня в семье великой,
В семье вольной, новой
Не забудьте — помяните
Добрым, тихим словом.

Тарас Г. Шевченко

The Sleep

It has been years. Now I am home again
And see: the village has not changed;
It stagnates as of old in deadly sloth.
Some houses have no roofs. Some have no walls.
Same grime, same stench, same poverty and spleen,
Same slavish eyes, defiant now, now humble.
Yes, they are free—and their free arms
Hang limp just as the unfree did.
All is just as it was. Only in one respect
Have we outdone Asia, Europe, and the world:
Never before have my fellow countrymen
Slept with such a stupendous sleep.
They sleep all over, in villages, in towns,
In wagons, sleighs, by day and night, standing and sitting,
Merchant, official sleeps, the guard sleeps on duty,
Sleeps father, mother, and their children sleep,
Defendant sleeps, and his judge snores in bliss.
The peasants sleep; they harvest, plow, and sleep. They thresh
And sleep. Sleeps he who flogs, and whom they flog, he sleeps.
Only the tavern's open, its eyes never close.
And so, clutching a brandy bottle in her hand,
Her head against the Pole, her heel against Caucasian Mountains,
The Holy Russia sleeps with the deep sleep of earth.

Iván Sergéyevich Turgénev (1818-83)

Russian serfdom, degrading personally and damaging nationally, was abolished in 1861. But those who hoped that the emancipation would usher in a bright future were due for a disappointment. Nothing changed in the Russian village. Russia slept.

Сон

Давнёнько не бывал в стороне родной . . .
Но не нашёл я в ней заметной перемены.
Всё тот же мёртвенный, бессмысленный застой,
Строёния без крыш, разрушенные стёны,
И та же грязь, и вонь, и бёдность, и тоска,
И тот же рабский взгляд, то дёрзкий, то унылый!
Народ наш вольным стал, и вольная рука
Висит по-прёжнему какой-то плёткой хилой . . .
Всё, всё по-прёжнему! И только лишь в одном
Еврёпу, Азию, весь свет мы перегнали:
Нет! Никогда ещё таким ужасным сном
Мои любёзные соотчичи не спали!
Всё спит кругом, вездё, в дерёвнях, в городах,
В телёгах, на санях, днём, ночью, сидя, стоя . . .
Купёц, чиновник спит, спит сторож на часах,
И подсудимый спит, и дрыхнет судия,
Мертво спят мужики: жнут, пашут — спят; молотят —
Спят тоже . . . Спит отёц, спит мать, спит вся семья . . .
Все спят! Спит тот, кто бьёт, и тот, кого колотят!
Один царёв кабак — тот не смыкает глаз.
И, штоф с очищенной всей пятернёй сжимая,
Лбом в полюс уперший́сь, а пятками в Кавказ,
Спит непробудным сном отчизна, Русь святая.

Иван С. Тургёнев

March 19, 1823

You stood silent
Before me,
Your sad look was
Full of feeling,
It brought back
The lovely past.
It was the last one
In this world.

You went away
Like a silent angel;
Your grave is peaceful
Like paradise.
It holds all earthly
Remembrances,
It holds all holy
Thoughts of heaven.

Stars of heaven—
Silent night. . .

Vasíly Andréyevich Zhukóvsky

19 марта 1823

Ты предо мною
Стояла тихо.
Твой взор унылый
Был полон чувства.
Он мне напомнил
О милом прошлом . . .
Он был последним
На здешнем свете.

Ты удалилась
Как тихий ангел,
Твоя могила
Как рай спокойна!
Там все земные
Воспоминанья,
Там все святые
О небе мысли.

Звёзды небес,
Тихая ночь.

Василий А. Жуковский

The Provider

(Selection from "The Peasant Children")

Once in a cold winter time
I came out of the forest; the frost was bitter.
I look: slowly up the hill
Comes a worn-out horse, pulling a cart of wood,
And walking gravely, with a sedate calm
A peasant leads the horse by the bridle,
In big boots, in shaggy coat of sheepskin,
In huge mittens,—and himself a tot.
"Greetings, boy."—
                            "Get out of my way!"
"Oh, you do scare me, the very sight of you.
Where did you get the wood?"—
                            "In the forest, don't you see?
Father's cutting, and I cart it."
(From the forest I heard an ax chopping.)
"You have a big family?"
"Yep. But there are only two men—father and I..."
"Oh, I see. And what's your name?"—
                            "Vlas."
"How old are you?"—
                            "Just passed six.
Well, move on, you snail!" he gruffly chid the horse,
Pulled the bridle, walked a little faster.

Nikoláy Alexéyevich Nekrásov (1821-78; with many of his contemporaries he understood literature as a tool of social criticism).

Thanks to an unusual power of empathy, the Russian social critic did not need to sensationalize to arouse his audience. This simple realistic scene spoke more eloquently against child labor than the American "muckrakers".

Кормилец

Однажды, в студёную зимнюю пору
Я из лесу вышел. Был сильный мороз,
Гляжу, поднимается медленно в гору
Лошадка, везущая хворосту воз.
И, шествуя важно, в спокойствии чинном,
Лошадку ведёт под уздцы мужичок
В больших сапогах, в полушубке овчинном,
В больших рукавицах... а сам с ноготок!
— Здорово, парнище! —
                                    «Ступай себе мимо!
— Уж больно ты грозен, как я погляжу!
Откуда дровишки? —
                                    Из лесу, вестимо:
Отец, слышишь, рубит, а я отвожу.
(В лесу раздавался топор дровосека).
— А что, у отца-то большая семья? —
«Семья-то большая, да два человека
Всего мужиков-то: отец мой и я...»
— Так вон оно что! А как звать тебя? —
                                    «Власом».
— А кой тебе годик? —
                                    Шестой миновал...
Ну, мёртвая! — крикнул малюточка басом,
Рванул под уздцы и быстрей зашагал.

Николай А. Некрасов

In Full Blaze the Labor in the Fields

In full blaze the labor in the fields. . .
Oh, the lot of the Russian woman!
It would be hard to find a harder one.
No wonder you grow old before your time,
You, sorrowful mother
Of the all-suffering Russian race.

Unbearable heat; a treeless plain,
Meadows and fields, endless horizon—
The sun burns without mercy.
With her last strength a wretched woman toils,
A cloud of gnats sways to and fro above her,
They sting her and gibe her and buzz.
Lifting the heavy plough
She cut her bare foot—
In vain she tried to stanch the blood.

From the neighboring patch there comes a cry—
She runs, her hair is flying,
She must rock the baby.
Well, why do you stand over him all in a daze?
Sing him the song of eternal suffering,
Sing, you patient mother!

Are those tears on your eyelashes, or drops of sweat?
It's hard to say.
They fall into the jug
Plugged with a dirty rag. No matter!

В полном разгаре страда деревенская

В по́лном разга́ре страда́ деревéнская . . .
До́ля ты! — ру́сская до́люшка жéнская!
Вряд ли труднéе сыска́ть.
Не мудрено́, что ты вя́нешь до врéмени,
Всёвыноси́щего ру́сского плéмени

Многострада́льная мать!
Зной нестерпи́мый: равни́на безлéсная,
Ни́вы, поко́сы, да ширь поднебéсная —
Со́лнце неща́дно пали́т.
Бéдная ба́ба из сил выбива́ется,
Столб насеко́мых над ней колыха́ется,
Жа́лит, щеко́чет, жужжи́т!
Приподнима́я косу́лю тяжёлую,
Ба́ба порéзала но́женьку го́лую —
Нéкогда кровь унима́ть!

Слы́шится крик у сосéдней поло́сыньки,
Ба́ба туда́ — растрепа́лися ко́сыньки, —
На́до ребёнка кача́ть!
Что же ты ста́ла над ним в отупéнии?
Пой ему́ пéсню о вéчном терпéнии,
Пой, терпели́вая мать!

Слёзы ли, пот ли у ней над ресни́цею,
Пра́во, сказа́ть мудрено́.
В жбан э́тот, за́ткнутый гря́зной тряпи́цею,
Ка́нут они́ — всё равно́!

She puts the brim of the jug
To her parched lips.
Do they taste good, your tears,
Mixed with thin soup, in the heat of the fields?

Nikoláy Alexéyevich Nekrásov (1821-78)

*In 1863, two years after the emancipation of the serfs,
Nekrásov penned this scene strikingly similar to Shevchénko's
"Harvestwoman". But there is a difference. Shevchénko's serf
finds a moment of happiness in her dream about the future
freedom of her son. For Nekrásov's free woman the overseer
is gone, but so is the hope that freedom will bring happiness.
Her toil and suffering have not changed.*

Вот она́ гу́бы свои́ опалённые
Жа́дно подно́сит к края́м . . .
Вку́сны ли, ми́лая, слёзы солёные
С ки́слым кваско́м пополáм?

Никола́й А. Некра́сов

Silentium

Be still, and hide, and veil
Your feelings and your dreams,
Let them rise and set
In the depth of soul,
Bright stars in the night:
Delight in them, be still.
Can heart explain itself?
Another understand?
Another see what gives you life?
A thought, once spoken, is a lie.
Disclosing them, you roil the springs:
Drink them alone, and silent be.
Know how to live within yourself.
A universe is hidden in your soul
Of secret, of enchanted thoughts
Which outward noise will suffocate,
The rays of day will render blind.
Hark to their songs, and silent be.

Fëdor Ivánovich Tyútchev (1803-73)

A number of Russian writers, weary of the irony, agitations, and contradictions of their society, withdrew into the realm of inner contemplation, mysticism, symbolism. Tyútchev's poem contains one of the most radical thoughts of this movement: "A thought, once spoken, is a lie."

Silentium

Молчи́, скрыва́йся и та́й
И чу́вства и мечты́ свои́!
Пуска́й в душе́вной глубине́
И всхо́дят, и зайду́т оне́,
Как звёзды я́сные в ночи́:
Любу́йся и́ми, и молчи́.
Как се́рдцу вы́сказать себя́?
Друго́му как поня́ть тебя́?
Поймёт ли он, чем ты живёшь?
Мысль изречённая есть ложь.
Взрыва́я возмути́шь ключи́,
Пита́йся и́ми и молчи́!
Лишь жить в само́м себе́ уме́й!
Есть це́лый мир в душе́ твое́й
Таи́нственно волше́бных дум.
Их заглуши́т нару́жный шум,
Дневны́е ослепя́т лучи́:
Внима́й их пе́нью — и молчи́!

Фёдор И. Тютчев

Fires Ahead 74

Once on a dark autumn night I rode in a boat on a gloomy Siberian river. Suddenly, in the bend of the river before us, under the dark mountains, we saw a little fire.

Its flame leapt up so clearly that it seemed quite near.

"Thanks, Lord!" I said delighted. "A village is just ahead, we will put up for the night."

My oarsman—a Siberian—turned, looked over his shoulder at the fire and again bent impassively over the oars.

"Far."

I did not believe him: there was the fire, coming at us from the thick darkness. And yet he was right; we had to go yet very far.

Those night fires seem to draw near, conquer the darkness, dance, promise, and deceive. They look as if you could reach them with one or two strokes of the oars, as if the trip were over. And yet—they are far.

We rode for a long time down the gloomy, murky river. Ravines and boulders swam out of the darkness, reared above us, and swam into night again, disappearing in the endless distance. And the fire was burning ahead, dancing and deceiving, so close and so far.

I remember often that dark river in the shadow of rocky mountains, and that dancing fire. Many other fires have teased me with their nearness before and since. But life flows between

Как-то давно, тёмным осенним вечером случилось мне плыть по угрюмой сибирской реке. Вдруг на повороте реки, впереди, под тёмными горами мелькнул огонёк.

Мелькнул ярко, сильно, близко...

— Ну, слава Богу! — сказал я с радостью, — деревня, близко ночлег!

Гребец-сибиряк повернулся, посмотрел через плечо на огонь и опять апатично налёг на весло.

— Далече!

Я не поверил: огонёк так и стоял, выступая вперёд из неопределённой тьмы. Но гребец был прав: оказалось, действительно, далеко.

Свойство этих ночных огней приближаться, побеждая тьму, и сверкать, и обещать и манить своею близостью. Кажется, вот-вот ещё два-три удара веслом — и путь кончен... А между тем — далеко...

И долго мы плыли по угрюмой и мрачной, как чернила реке. Ущелья и скалы выплывали, надвигались и уплывали, оставаясь назади и теряясь, казалось, в бесконечной дали, а огонёк всё стоял впереди, переливаясь и маня, всё так же близко и всё так же далеко.

Мне часто вспоминается теперь и эта тёмная река, затенённая скалистыми горами, и этот живой огонёк. Много огней и раньше, и после манили не одного меня своею близостью. Но — жизнь течёт всё в тех же угрюмых бере-

the same murky banks, and the fires are far. And we must bend over our oars.

And yet—there are fires ahead!

Vladímir Galaktiónovich Korolénko (1853-1921)

Toward the end of the 19th century, Russians were torn between their own inertia and the hopes and fears of the coming revolution. Korolénko, the lyricist of the Siberian forests, veiled the awesome realities of revolution with the romantic longing for the "fires ahead."

га́х, а огни́ ещё далеко́. И опя́ть прихо́дится налега́ть на вёсла.

Но всё-таки... всё-таки впереди́ — огни́!

Влади́мир Г. Короле́нко

The Night Was All Aglow

The night was all aglow. The orchard full of moon.
The flame was dying on the glowing grate.
You sang until the dawn, growing weak with your tune,
That you are all my love; I have no other fate.

And many years have passed, all wearying and sad,
And in the silent night again I hear your voice.
It wafts again, as once, its sorrowful ballade
That you are all my love, I have no other joys.

*Afanásy Afanásevich Fet (1820-92; the highest ambition
of his sweet, melodious lyrics was "to bring the reader a rose").*

Сияла ночь...

Сияла ночь. Луно́й был по́лон сад. Лежа́ли
Лучи́ у на́ших ног в гости́ной без огне́й.
Мы пе́ли до зари́, в слеза́х изнемога́ли,
Что ты одна́ любо́вь, ино́й нет в жи́зни всей.

И мно́го лет прошло́, томи́тельных и ску́чных,
И вот в тиши́ ночно́й твой го́лос слы́шу вновь —
И ве́ет, как тогда́, во вздо́хах э́тих зву́чных,
Что ты одна́ вся жизнь, что ты одна́ любо́вь.

Афана́сий А. Фет

Loneliness

A lady's companion, emaciated, a foreigner,
Was bathing in the sea on a cold evening,
Waiting and hoping that someone would see her
Running, half naked,
With her bathing suit clinging to her body, from the surf.
Then, putting on a beach mantle,
She sat down on the sand, ate plums,
And a huge dog with rumbling bark
Jumped into water foaming up the beach
And with his hot mouth happily he caught
The black ball which she threw into the water
Shouting: "Hop!"
         From afar
Came the beams of a lighthouse like a radiant star. . .
The sand grew damp, the moon rose in the sky,
And on the waters close to shore, a green reflection
Glittered and broke. . . On the dunes behind
Against the light sky, a black lonely bench.
There stood a while, with his hat taken off,
A writer, coming from his supper.
He smoked a cigar, with a grin
He thought: "In that striped bathing suit
She looks just like a zebra."

    *Iván Alexéyevich Búnin (1870-1953; winner of Nobel.
Prize for literature in 1933).*

    *Russian genius at its best. In this little realistic scene the
title, third line, and Writer's comment at the end produce an
excruciating pathos.*

Одиночество

Худа́я компаньо́нка, иностра́нка,
Купа́лась в мо́ре ве́чером холо́дным
И всё ждала́, что кто́-нибудь уви́дит,
Как вы́бежит она́, полунага́я,
В трико́, прили́пшем к те́лу, из прибо́я.
Пото́м, наде́в широ́кий балахо́н,
Сиде́ла на песке́ и е́ла сли́вы,
А кру́пный пёс с греми́щим ла́ем пры́гал
В прибре́жнюю сире́невую ки́пень
И жа́ркой па́стью ра́достно кида́лся
На чёрный мяч, кото́рый с кри́ком «Нор!»
Она́ швыря́ла в во́ду . . . Загоре́лся
Вдали́ мая́к лучи́стою звездо́й . . .
Сыре́л песо́к, взошла́ луна́ над мо́рем,
И по вода́м у бе́рега лома́лся,
Сверка́л зелёный гля́нец . . . На обры́ве,
Что возвыша́лся сза́ди, в све́тлом не́бе,
Черне́ла одино́кая скамья́ . . .
Там постоя́л с раскры́той голово́ю
Писа́тель, пообе́давший в гостя́х,
Сига́ру покури́л и, усмехну́вшись,
Поду́мал: — Полоса́тое трико́
Её на зе́бру де́лало похо́жей.

Ива́н А. Бу́нин

Pluckily the Girl faces Death,
She is waiting for the fatal blow.
Death is fretting, pitying her victim:
"Now, just look at that, how young you are!
Did you have to be rude to a Czar?"
"Don't be angry," gave the Girl her answer,
"My love kissed me for the very first time
Under the green elderberry bushes.
For the Czar what did I care just then?
Well, the Czar, as if to spite us,
Was returning from his wars. I told him:
'Go away from here, O Father Czar!'
I spoke with the best intention,
But it came out badly, see!
Well, it can't be helped. No man escapes you.
I guess I will die with love unsated.
Sister Death! With all my soul I beg you,
Let me kiss him just once more."
Strange were such words to Death,
No one asks such things from Death!
Yet she thinks: "How will I make my living
If people should cease to kiss each other?"
Her bones warming in the rays of sun
She said: "Kiss away, but make it snappy.
Night belongs to you, you die at dawn."
Much more than a full day has now passed
And the Girl is not coming back.
That is bad. Death does not feel like joking.

Девушка и смерть

Дéвушка стои́т пред Смéртью смéло
Грóзного удáра ожидáя.
Смерть бормóчет — жéртву пожалéла:
— Ишь ты ведь, какáя молодáя!
Что ты нагруби́ла там царю́?
Я тебя́ за э́то уморю́! —
— Не серди́сь, — отвéтила деви́ца, —
За что на меня́ тебé серди́ться?
Целовáл меня́ впервы́е ми́лый
Под кустóм зелёной бузины́, —
До царя́ ли мне в ту пóру бы́ло?
Ну, а царь — на грех — бежи́т с войны́.
Я и говорю́ емý, царю́,
Отойди́, мол, бáтюшка, отсю́да!
Хорошó, как бýдто, говорю́,
А — гляди́-ко, вы́шло то как хýдо,
Что ж?! От Смéрти нéкуда девáться,
Ви́дно, я умрý не   долюбя́.
Смéртушка! Душóй прошý тебя́ —
Дай ты мне ещё поцеловáться. —
Стрáнны бы́ли Смéрти рéчи э́ти, —
Смерть об э́том никогдá не прóсят!
Дýмает: Чем бýду жить на свéте,
Éсли лю́ди целовáться брóсят?
И на вéшнем сóлнце кóсти грéя,
Смерть сказáла, подмани́в змею́:
— Ну, ступáй, целýйся, да скорéе!
Ночь твоя́, а на зарé — убью́!

Getting angrier and wilder by the minute
Death puts on her leggings and her sandals,
Hardly waiting for the moonlit night,
And sets out, more ominous than clouds of autumn;
Walks an hour, sees: there in a thicket
Under young and dewy hazel bushes
Sits the girl like a nymph of spring,
With his head between her knees
Sleeps a youth, a worn-out stag. . .
Death looks at them, and the flames of anger
Softly die out in her barren head.
"Why did you, like Eve,
Hide from God behind a bush?"
Shielding her love with her starlit body
As if covering him with the sky
Gave the Girl her answer: "Wait, don't scold me,
Don't make noise, don't startle the poor boy.
I'll go right away and lie down in the grave,
But him, spare him yet.
I am guilty, did not keep my word.
Let me hug him just once more:
How he loves to be with me!
And I love him, too. . . When my love hugs me,
There is no earth and there is no heaven,
And my soul is full of strength not of this earth,
And my soul burns with a flame not of this world."
Death is silent. The words of the Girl
Flood her bones with fires of envy,
Now they burn with fever, now they freeze with ague.
Death is not a mother, but she is a woman,
And her heart is stronger than her reason.
"Well," Death said, "let that miracle happen!

Уж прошло́ гора́здо бо́льше су́ток,
А — не возвраща́ется деви́ца.
Это — пло́хо. Сме́рти не до шу́ток.

Становля́сь всё зле́е и жесто́че,
Смерть обу́ла ла́пти и ону́чи
И едва́ дожда́вшись лу́нной но́чи,
В путь идёт, грозне́й осе́нней ту́чи.

Час прошла́ и ви́дит: в переле́ске,
Под роси́стой молодо́й оре́шней,
На траве́ атла́сной в лу́нном бле́ске
Де́вушка сиди́т боги́ней ве́шней.

Положи́в ей го́лову в коле́ни,
Дре́млет па́рень, как оле́нь уста́лый.
Смерть гляди́т — и ти́хо пла́мя гне́ва
Га́снет в её че́репе пусто́м.

— Ты чего́ же э́то сло́вно Е́ва
Спря́талась от Бо́га за кусто́м?

То́чно не́бом — лу́нно-звёздным те́лом
Ми́лого от Сме́рти заслоня́,
Отвеча́ет ей деви́ца сме́ло:

— Погоди́-ко, не руга́й меня́!
Не шуми́, не испуга́й бедня́гу,
Остро́ю косо́ю не звени́!
Я сейча́с приду́, в моги́лу ля́гу,
А его́ — подо́льше сохрани́!

Винова́та — не пришла́ я к сро́ку,
Дай ещё парни́шку обниму́:
Бо́льно хорошо́ со мной ему́!

Да и он хоро́ш! Обни́мет ми́лый,
Ни земли́, ни не́ба бо́льше нет.
И душа́ полна́ незде́шней си́лой,
И гори́т в душе́ незде́шний свет. —

I will let you live. But I'll be always with you,
Eternally I'll be close to Love."
From that time on, Love and Death, like sisters,
Have been truest friends until our days;
After Love comes Death with her sharp weapon,
Trudges after her enchanted,
Everywhere, at weddings and wakes,
Constantly and infallibly working
Joys of Love and Happiness of Life.

Maxím Górky (1868-1936)

Górky is known in the West for his social criticism in The Lower Depths *and revolutionary ideas in* Mother. *Such attitudes were only an expression of his great passion for life and beauty. His long poem "Death and the Girl" treats an idea suggested in Vyázemski's "Winter": Life and Death are inseparable. Whereas the pre-Gorkian poets were melancholy in their merriest moments—"Even though Life is beautiful, there is Death!"—Górky is vigorously optimistic: "Life is beautiful exactly because there is Death."*

Смерть молчи́т, а де́вушкины ре́чи
За́висти огнём ей ко́сти пла́вят,
Смерть не мать, но — же́нщина, и в ней
Се́рдце то́же ра́зума сильне́й;
— Что ж, — сказа́ла Смерть, — пусть бу́дет чудо!
Разреша́ю я тебе́ — живи́!
То́лько я с тобо́ю ря́дом бу́ду,
Ве́чно бу́ду о́коло Любви́. —
С той поры́ Любо́вь и Смерть, как сёстры,
Хо́дят неразлу́чно до сего́ дня,
За Любо́вью Смерть с косо́ю о́строй
Та́щится повсю́ду то́чно сво́дня.
Хо́дит, околдо́вана сестро́ю,
И везде́ — на сва́дьбе и на три́зне —
Неуста́нно, неукло́нно стро́ит
Ра́дости Любви́ и сча́стье Жи́зни.

Макси́м Го́рький

Dying Mother

"Is she dead?"—"Speak softly, softly:
Maybe she just naps a little."
One suggested: "Bring the child,
Put him on her breast."

Where the heart had throbbed,
Tearful child now hid his face;
If she did not wake that moment,
It's the end; you pray for her.

A. N. Apúkhtin (1841-93) wrote lyrics full of sweet melancholy.

Умирающая мать

— Что, умерла? —
                        — Потише говорите:
Быть может, удалось на время ей заснуть. —
И кто́-то предложил: — Ребёнка принесите
И положите ей на грудь! —

И вот на месте том, где прежде сердце билось,
Ребёнок с плачем скрыл лицо своё . . .
И если она теперь не пробудилась —
Всё кончено, молитесь за неё!

А. Н. Апухтин

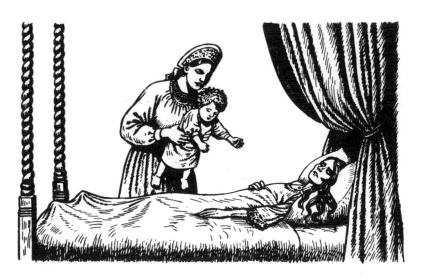

I Am Fainting (Selections)

I am fainting with weariness,
My soul is wounded, bleeds.
Is there no pity for us?
Is there no love for us?

Without protests, without wonder
We do all that our fate bids us.
He who made us without fire,
Having made us, could not love us.

And we fall, a feeble host,
Feebly hoping for miracles.
Like the slab on a fresh grave
Falls on us the voiceless sky.

Zinaída Hippius (1869-1945) gave voice to the decadent hopelessness of those who did not share Górky's optimism or did not find refuge in the mystical contemplation of their souls.

Изнемогаю от усталости

Изнемога́ю от уста́лости,
Душа́ изра́нена в крови́.
Уже́ли нет над на́ми жа́лости,
Уже́ль над на́ми нет любви́?

Без ро́пота, без удивле́ния,
Мы де́лаем, что хо́чет рок.
Кто со́здал нас без вдохнове́ния,
Тот полюби́ть, созда́в, не мог.

Мы па́даем, толпа́ бесси́льная,
Бесси́льно ве́ря в чудеса́,
А све́рху, как плита́ моги́льная,
Глухи́е да́вят небеса́.

Зинаи́да Ги́ппиус

When Haunted by Insistent Anguish

When haunted by insistent anguish
You walk into a dome and stand in silence,
Lost in the immense crowd
Like a fragment of one suffering soul.

Your anguish drowns imperceptibly,
And you feel that your spirit, suddenly, mysteriously,
Has poured into its native sea
And, made one with it, storms the gates of heaven.

Apollón Nikoláyevich Máykov (1821-97) describes one of the most dangerous ideas in European philosophy: that the individual is of no value except as part of the collective of the people. This is the romantic version of the unity of life (compare Turgénev's "The Dog"). It was the philosophical basis of National Socialism in Germany and Communism in Russia.

Когда гоним тоской неутолимой

Когда́ гони́м тоско́й неутоли́мой
Войдёшь во храм и ста́нешь там в тиши́,
Поте́рянный в толпе́ необозри́мой,
Как часть одно́й страда́ющей души́:

Нево́льно в ней твоё пото́нет го́ре,
И чу́вствуешь, что дух твой вдруг влился́
Таи́нственно в своё родно́е мо́ре,
И за-одно́ с ним рвётся в небеса́.

Аполло́н Н. Ма́йков

Russia! My Russia! I see you, from my wondrous, beautiful distance I see you: all is wretched in your confines, disjointed, uneasy. There are no wonders of nature to delight and overwhelm the sight, and no wonders of art to crown them. All is open, all is barren, all is desert in you. Almost unnoticeable stand your lowly towns in the plains; nothing entices, nothing charms the eye.

And yet, what mysterious power draws me to you? Why do I hear in my ears your melancholy song which rings across you far and wide from sea to sea? What does it say, this song? What calls, what weeps, what clutches at my heart? What are these sounds which blandish me and enter me and entwine my heart? Russia! What do you ask from me?

And while I yet stand in confusion, without motion, a stormy cloud has cast a shadow over my head, heavy with threatening rain, and my thoughts have grown silent before your immense space. What future presage your boundless horizons? Should not endless thoughts be born here, since you yourself are endless? Should not your people be heroes, since they have room for heroic deeds? How luminous, how full of wonder, how ineffable are your distant ends, O Russia!

Nikoláy Vasílevich Gógol (1809-52)

Although the novel Dead Souls *was written in 1836, these words selected from it speak as powerfully to Russian hearts today as they did a century and a half ago. They are an expression of faith that when the storms of time have passed, the future of the country cannot but be glorious.*

Русь

Русь! Русь! Ви́жу тебя́, из моего́ чу́дного, прекра́сного далека́ тебя́ ви́жу. Бе́дно, разбро́сано и неприю́тно в тебе́. Не развеселя́т, не испуга́ют взо́ра де́рзкие ди́ва приро́ды, венча́ные де́рзкими ди́вами иску́сства. Откры́то, пусты́нно и ровно́ всё в тебе́; как то́чки, как значки́, непримéтно торча́т среди́ равни́н не высо́кие твои́ города́; ничто́ не обольсти́т и не очару́ет взо́ра.

Но кака́я же непости́жимая, та́йная си́ла влечёт к тебе́? Почему́ слы́шится и раздаётся в у́шах твоя́ тоскли́вая, несу́щаяся по всей длине́ и ширине́ твое́й, от мо́ря до мо́ря, пе́сня? Что в ней, в э́той пе́сне? Что зовёт, и рыда́ет и хвата́ет за се́рдце? Каки́е зву́ки болéзненно лобза́ют и стремя́тся в ду́шу и вью́тся о́коло моего́ се́рдца? Русь! Чего́ же ты хо́чешь от меня́?

И ещё по́лный недоумéния, неподви́жно стою́ я, а уже́ го́лову осени́ло гро́зное о́блако, тяжёлое гряду́щими дождя́ми, и онемéла мысль пред твои́м простра́нством. Что проро́чит сей необъя́тный просто́р? Здесь ли, в тебé ли не роди́ться беспредéльной мы́сли, когда́ ты сама́ без конца́? Здесь ли не быть богатырю́, когда́ есть мéсто, где разверну́ться и пройти́сь ему́? У! кака́я сверка́ющая, чу́дная, незнако́мая землé даль! Русь!

Никола́й В. Го́голь

Index

Указатель